Beautiful Brown Child

<3 = ♥

DEAR BEAUTIFUL BROWN CHILD

Nichelle Joi
Age 14

Illustrated by: Jacqui Smith

© 2021 All rights reserved
ISBN 978-1-943343-21-8

Published by:
Destined To Publish
773-783-2981
www.DestinedToPublish.com

DEDICATION

To my *"little siblings"*

Yarri A.
Soni A.-S.
Kylie, Karis & Joriah A.
Mira & Arim B.
Jaice, Xia, J'uelz, & Aspen B.
Emanuel B.
Kylie B.
River B.
Trinity & Tatum B.
India C.
Kameron, Khristian & Kendall C.
Ke'Mari & Ky'Ryn C.
Kace & Tula Grace D.
Brendon E.
Supria & Seth F.
Brooke G.
Kassie G.
Justina, JaKayla & Jalissa H.

Angelis H.-D.
Reign & Cannon J.
Johnathan J.
Jael, Jon, Jaia, Judah, Jax & Jalen J.
D'emetrius J.
Josiah R.-J.
Kennedi & Aubree M.
Jordyn M.
Selena M.
Ameiah R.
Ever S.
Zoe, Kaleb, TC & Miles S.
Makenna, Gianna & Dominic T.
Braylen T.
Dakota T.
Naomi T.
Matthius W.
Adele W.

And to *every* Beautiful Brown Child,
you are all beautiful in every way!

I love you all so much
and I hope you enjoy.

To
Mrs. Sharon Cruikshank,
you were such a kind soul.
I will miss our quick encounters,
your wonderful smile, warm hugs,
and your amazing writings.

I wish we were able
to have more time together.
I miss you so much.

Rest in heaven <3
Nichelle Joi

<3 = ❤

INTRODUCTION

Growing up as a black girl in a predominantly white neighborhood and school, it was difficult for me to build self-confidence and see myself as beautiful when I was younger, especially because at the time, the "beauty standards" were very clearly the opposite of a black girl.

Being told by my own classmates at the age of six or seven that "your hair looks funny" when it was in twists and barrettes, or that "your lips are too big" or "your nose is really large," really took a toll on me and used to have me wishing that I was more like a white girl, with long, straight hair that I couldn't sweat out, pale, fair skin, and long, skinny limbs that wouldn't be considered "thick" or "chubby."

It's only recently that I've found beauty in being black and become completely comfortable in myself, appreciating every aspect of my black features.

After the events of 2020, it can be hard to find self-worth when people are arguing over the costs of your life and the lives of those who look like you. But by writing this book, I hope it becomes the representation that I didn't have as a child, and that it uplifts today's youth to let them know how amazing it is for them to be children of color.

So, I hope this book is something that is easy to come to whenever a child is feeling like they aren't as amazing as they really are.

With that being said, happy Black History Month, happy Asian American/Pacific Islander Month, happy Indigenous Peoples' Day, happy disabled awareness month, and I wish great celebrations onto any other memorial holidays/months.

Embrace all of who you are, and don't forget to love others, but most importantly, love yourself.

Thanks for reading.

Last but not least, I would like to greatly thank my parents, Joey & Marilyn, for being with me through anything and everything, pushing me when I needed it, and dealing with all of my crazy stuff last minute when I really needed something.

I have no clue where our family would be without both of you, and you have no clue how much I appreciate you both.

When I am famous, the first people I have to thank will be you for providing everything I needed to expand my gifts and talents.

I love you more than words are worth!
Nichelle <3

Beautiful Brown Child

Dear Beautiful Brown Child,
Your smile is so bright!
It brings joy in the day
and it lights up the night.

Never stop smiling,
no matter what.
Don't let people
bring you down,
don't let that smile shut!

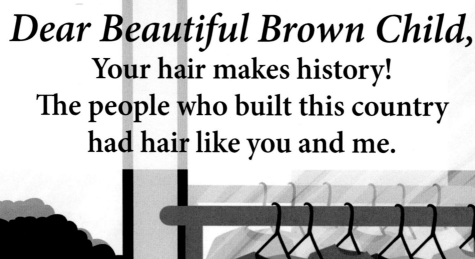

Dear Beautiful Brown Child,
Your hair makes history!
The people who built this country
had hair like you and me.

Some have short hair,
some have long,
some people choose
not to show it.
But your hair is rare,
and it is unique,
I really hope you know it!

BLACK LIVES MATTER

Dear Beautiful Brown Child,
Your skin is not a threat!
It's magnificent and unique to you,
don't ever forget!

It may be dark, light, or in between,
your skin is the most stunning trait
the world has ever seen!

Dear Beautiful Brown Child,
Your body is wonderfully beautiful!
It can run, it can dance,
it can even be musical!

It doesn't matter if you're
tall or short, chubby or thin,
your body is marvelous,
as amazing as you are within!

Dear Beautiful Brown Child,
Your eyes are bright like the sun!
They help you do things like
jump and play and run.

Some people are born with sight,
others, however, are not,
but both people are beautiful
no matter what you're taught.

Dear Beautiful Brown Child,
Be thankful for what you've got!
Not every child has what you have,
so give that a hard thought.

You have those who care about you,
who always want the best.
So make sure you thank them,
don't leave their love unaddressed!

Dear Beautiful Brown Child,
Your imagination is endless!
You're able to become anything,
your every thought is tremendous!

Use your imagination
to create your heart's desire.
Never lose your train of thought,
and don't put out that fire!

Dear Beautiful Brown Child,
Your brain is so smart!
At times it may seem
you don't know where to start.

But you've gotten this far with your smart brain, right? Use it to achieve your goals, and be what you want in life!

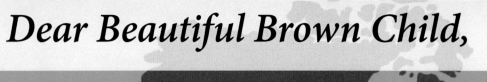

Dear Beautiful Brown Child,

Do you know how beautiful you are?
So radiant and bright,
your light shines like a star!

You are smart, you are strong,
you are brilliant and kind.
Don't ever be afraid to say what's on your mind!

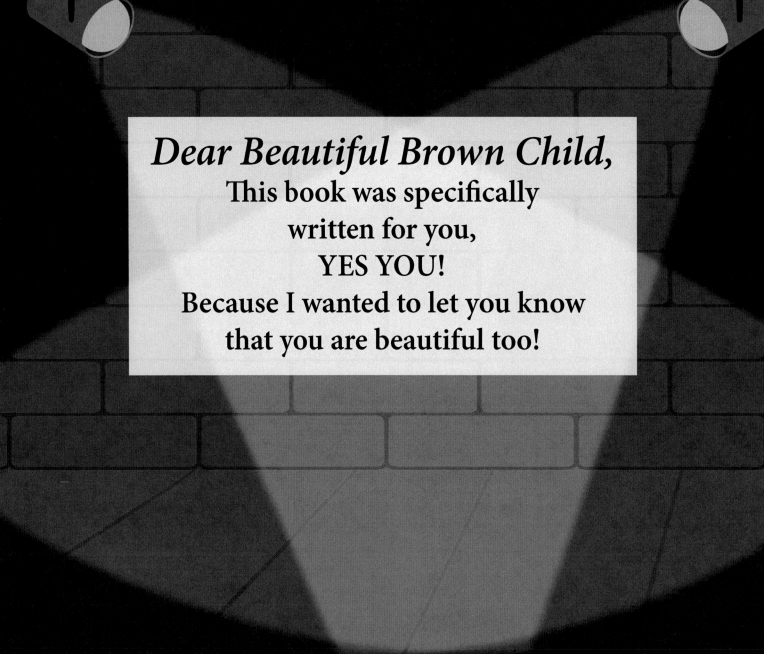

Dear Beautiful Brown Child,
This book was specifically
written for you,
YES YOU!
Because I wanted to let you know
that you are beautiful too!

Don't take your beauty for granted,
know that this is true.

Dear Beautiful Brown Child,
I'm so glad that you are you!

My Name Is

_____

I am _____ years old.

My favorite color(s) is _____.

Use your favorite color(s) to fill in the box.

The people in my family include:

_____.

Draw a picture of your family below.

This is my self portrait:

Draw a picture of yourself below.

See how cool I am?

My favorite things about me are: _____

_____

_____

_____

_____

_____

Because: _____

_____

_____

_____

_____

I am in the _____ grade.

My favorite subjects in school are:

_____.

When I grow up I want to be _____.

Draw a picture of yourself in your future career.

My favorite sport is _____.

The places I have traveled to are:

_____

_____.

My hobbies are:

_____

_____.

My favorite song is _____.

By _____.

My favorite movie is _____.

My favorite celebrity is _____.

If I could be in any movie it would be:

_____.

The character I would like to play would be:

_____.

My favorite author is _____.

My favorite books are:

_____

If I could be in any book it would be:

_____.

The character I would like to play would be:

_____.

My pet(s) name is _____.

Draw your favorite animal here

My favorite food is _____.

Draw your favorite food here

My favorite candy or dessert is _____.

Draw a picture of your favorite candy or dessert here.

AFFIRMATION

af·firm·a·tion

/ˌafərˈmāSH(ə)n/

noun

plural noun: affirmations

[+ object]

1. *formal*: to say that something is true in a confident way

2. *formal*: to show a strong belief in or dedication to (something, such as an important idea)

3. *law*: to decide that the judgment of another court is correct

I *affirm* that I am BEAUTIFUL!

Synonyms:

Assertion, declaration, statement, proclamation, pronouncement, oath, vow, guarantee, promise, pledge, confirmation, defense.

DAILY AFFIRMATIONS

- I am AWESOME!

- I am smart!

- I am strong!

- I can do anything I put my mind to!

- I am beautiful/handsome!

- I will not use the word "can't" to define my possibilities!

- My skin color, hair type, and physical features DO NOT DEFINE ME as a person!

- I am an extraordinary person, inside and out!

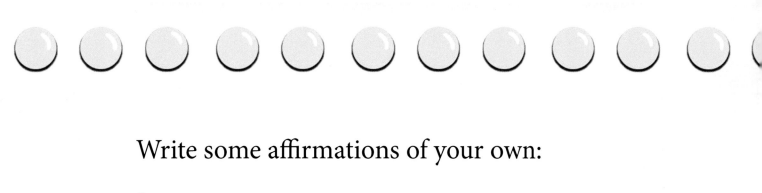

Write some affirmations of your own:

- _____

- _____

- _____

- _____

- _____

- _____

- _____

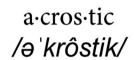

a·cros·tic
/əˈkrôstik/

noun

A poem, word puzzle, or other composition in which certain letters in each line form a word or words.

Here is my example of an acrostic.

N	is for	naturally talented
I	is for	iconic
C	is for	caring
H	is for	helpful
E	is for	excellent
L	is for	loving
L	is for	leader
E	is for	energetic
J	is for	joyful
O	is for	optimistic
I	is for	intelligent

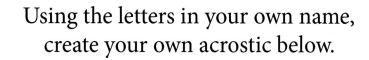

Using the letters in your own name,
create your own acrostic below.

_____ is for _____

_____ is for _____

_____ is for _____

_____ is for _____

_____ is for _____

_____ is for _____

_____ is for _____

_____ is for _____

_____ is for _____

_____ is for _____

_____ is for _____

_____ is for _____

What God's Word Says About Me!

I am loved and chosen

"Even before He made the world, God loved us and chose us in Christ to be holy and without fault in His eyes." *Ephesians 1:4*

I am beautifully created

"I praise you, for I am fearfully and wonderfully made. Wonderful are your works; my soul knows it very well." *Psalm 139:14*

I am never alone

"Don't be afraid, for I Am with you. Don't be discouraged, for I Am your God. I will strengthen you and help you. I will hold you up with My victorious right hand." *Isaiah 41:10*

Use these pages to write your thoughts!
What have you learned? How do you feel?

_____

_____

_____

_____

_____

_____

_____

_____

_____

_____

Fourteen-year-old Nichelle Joi enjoys reading, creative writing, and spending time with her family and friends.

She is an exceptional dancer and a talented violinist.

Nichelle is no novice to writing. Her two previous books, *The Joys of Writing: Short Stories for Kids* and *The Great Adventures: The Mystery of the Missing Artifacts*, were both written before she reached the age of ten. Both books were featured in the African American Literary Festival at Chicago's Harold Washington Library, as well as The Chicago Citizen newspaper.

She also adds to her writing credits the theme song for *Claudette's Miraculous Motown Adventure*, written for the First Lady of Motown, Claudette Robinson.

Currently Nichelle is a Sophomore in High School and lives in Illinois with her parents and older brother.

Other books by
Nichelle Joi

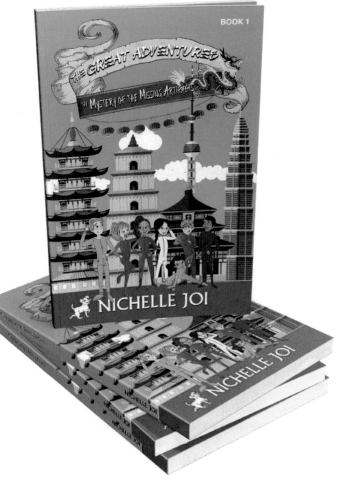

The Joys of Writing (paperback)
Short Stories for Kids.....................................$16.00
(Written at age 8) For readers Grades 3 and under

The Great Adventures (paperback)
The Mystery of the Missing Artifacts.......$14.00
(Written at age 9) For readers Grades 2 and over

Made in the USA
Monee, IL
01 August 2021

Is it a Fish?

By Alexander Chen and Andrew Chen

To Ms. Z,
$C_6H_{12}O_6$
Thank you for everything.
-Alex

Foreword

Our book, "Butterfly and Friends", was a hit. Our family was struggling to make a sequel. I was volunteering as a docent at a local aquarium, and it became an inside joke among my family to point at each tank and ask, "Is it a fish?"

Eventually, this book was born.

I hope you enjoy "Is It a Fish?"

This is a Pufferfish.

? ?

Is it a fish?

Yes! Pufferfish are fish!

However, not all things that live in the ocean are fish. Some are other types of animal.

This is a Starfish.

? **?**

Is it a fish?

No! Starfish aren't fish!

Fish have backbones. Starfish don't.
All starfish have five arms, and when
one gets cut off, it grows back!

This is a Jellyfish.

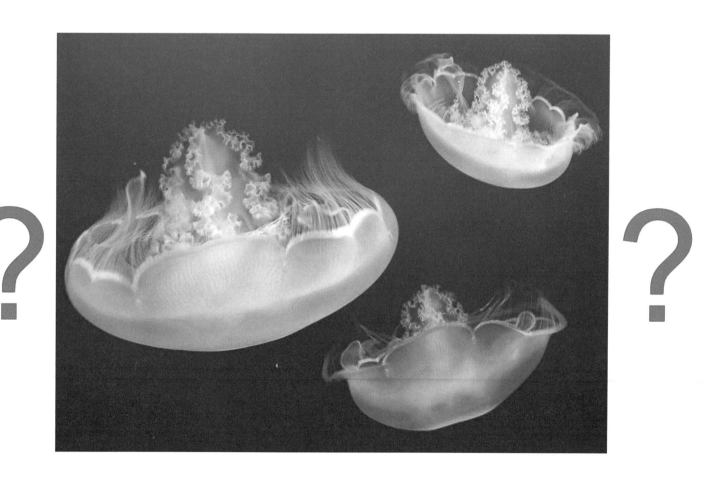

Is it a fish?

No! Jellyfish are not fish!

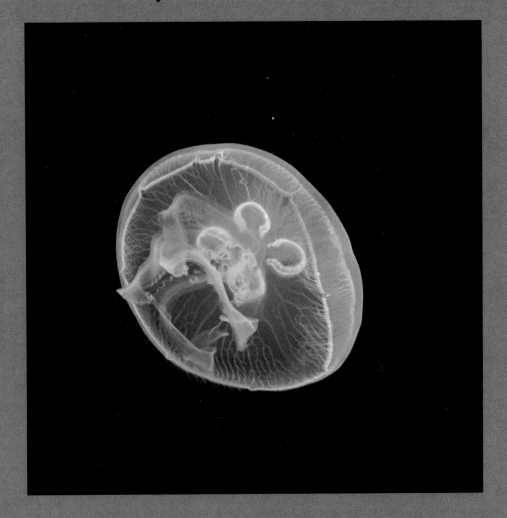

Jellyfish don't have backbones either.
Jellyfish actually can't swim! They are
pushed around by underwater rivers called
ocean currents.

This is a Seahorse.

?  ?

Is it a fish?

Yes! Seahorses are fish!

Seahorses are bad swimmers. They use their special tails not to swim, but to wrap themselves around kelp so they don't get blown away by ocean currents.

This is a Dolphin.

? ?

Is it a fish?

No! Dolphins are not fish!

Dolphins are mammals. Humans, cats, and dogs are also mammals. Dolphins and their cousins, the whales, have tails that go up and down.

This is a Shark.

Is it a fish?

Yes! Sharks are fish!

Sharks, like other fish, have tails that move side to side. Some people think that sharks eat people. Actually, most sharks avoid people.

This is a Stingray.

?  ?

Is it a fish?

Yes! Stingrays are fish!

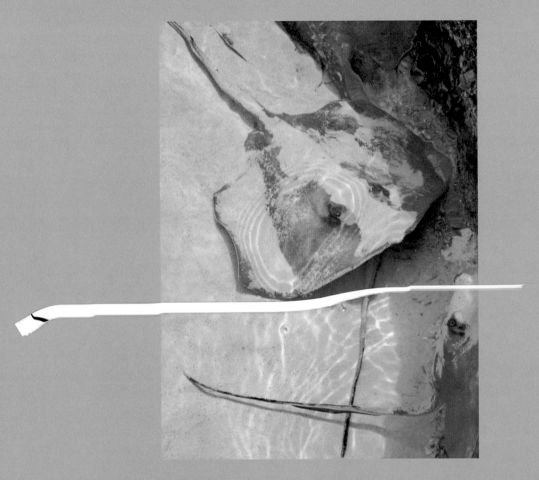

Stingrays actually are related to sharks!
Stingrays like to bury themselves in the
sand. Sometimes people accidentally step
on them. To avoid this, when treading in
shallow water, shuffle your feet forward
and don't take big steps.

This is a Sea Turtle.

Is it a fish?

No! Turtles aren't fish!

Turtles are reptiles, like crocodiles and snakes. Turtles are cold-blooded, meaning they can't get warm all by themselves. They need to lie in the sun to warm up.

This is an Eel.

Is it a fish?

Yes! Eels are fish!

Did you know? Eels have two jaws! One sits inside the other. When the eel eats, the jaw on the outside holds onto the food, while the one on the inside bites.

All animals, fish or not, are important to the ocean. We should respect all the amazing creatures that call our Earth home.

Ocean Facts for Adults:

The ocean covers two thirds of the surface of Earth and is home to 50-80% of all life on Earth, including microscopic organisms called phytoplankton. These are best thought of as really, really tiny plants. Huge colonies of phytoplankton, during photosynthesis, create most of the oxygen we breathe!

The ocean is also important in fighting climate change by absorbing half of the world's carbon. In fact, there is as much carbon in the ocean as there is in the atmosphere! However, extra carbon causes acidification of the ocean, which can make it hard for the shells of animals to form.

The ocean is full of wild and wonderful animals. It is important to keep our oceans safe, for their benefit, and ours too.

Also Available on Amazon:

BUTTERFLY AND FRIENDS

Made in the USA
Las Vegas, NV
11 February 2024